Theory Paper   Grade 6   2018   A

Duration 3 hours

Candidates should answer all FIVE questions.
Write your answers on this paper – no others will be accepted.
Answers must be written clearly and neatly – otherwise marks may be lost.

1   Answer ONE section only, (a) or (b).

15

EITHER

(a) Indicate ONE chord at each of the places marked * to accompany the following melody. You may do so by writing roman numerals or any other recognized method of notation between the staves, OR by writing notes on the staves which provide a proper harmonic structure; but use only ONE of these methods.

Traditional Norwegian Melody, 'Oslo' (adapted)

[Moderato]

OR

(b) Complete the bass line and add a suitable figured bass as necessary, **from the first beat of bar 3**, at the places marked ✳ in this passage. If you wish to use a $\frac{5}{3}$ chord, leave the space under the asterisk blank, but $\frac{5}{3}$ chords **must** be shown when used as part of a $\frac{6}{4}\frac{5}{3}$ progression or when chromatic alteration is required.

Handel, Aria from *Amadigi di Gaula* (adapted)

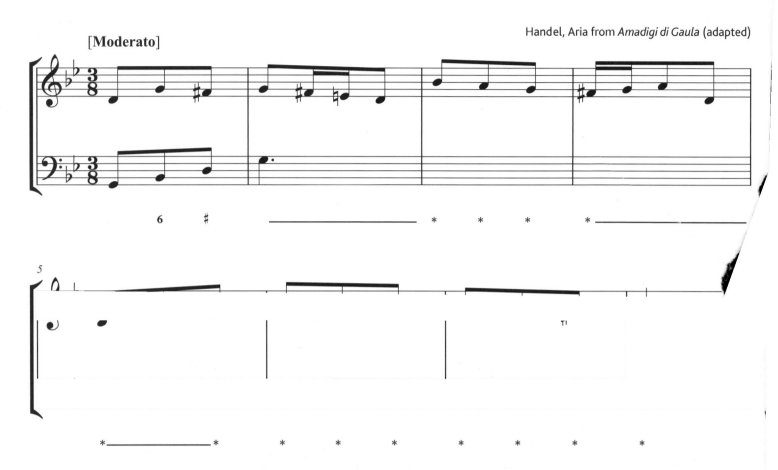

2 Writing for four-part voices (SATB) or keyboard, realize this figured bass.
   Assume that all chords are $\frac{5}{3}$ unless otherwise shown.

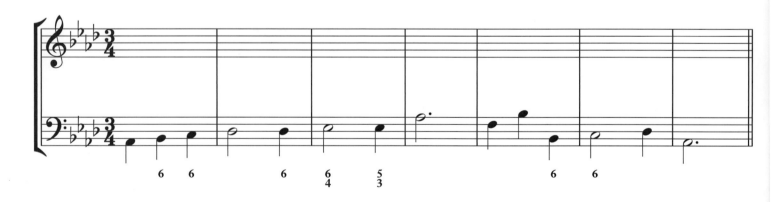

3 EITHER

(a) Continue this opening to form a complete melody for unaccompanied cello. It should end with a modulation to the dominant and should be between eight and ten bars long. Add performance directions as appropriate and write the complete melody on the staves below.

OR

(b) Continue this opening for unaccompanied flute to make a complete melody of not less than eight bars in length. You may make any modulation(s) that you wish, or none if you prefer. Add performance directions as appropriate and write the complete melody on the staves below.

Sehr langsam

Etwas langsamer

Im tempo

etc.

4 Look at the extract printed opposite, which is from a piano piece, and then answer the questions below.

(a) Give the meaning of **Sehr langsam**. .... (2)

(b) Write out in full the top right-hand part of bar 15 as you think it should be played. Part of the bar is given.

(3)

(c) Identify the chords marked * in bars 6 and 12 (both shaded) by writing on the dotted lines below. Use either words or symbols. For each chord, indicate the position and show whether it is major, minor, augmented or diminished.

Bar 6 .... Key   F major (3)

Bar 12 .... Key   A♭ major (3)

(d) Mark **clearly** on the score, using the appropriate capital letter for identification, one example of each of the following. Also give the bar number of each of your answers. The first answer is given.

In bars 1–8

A   a bar that has the same notes and rhythm as bar 1.   Bar .....5.....

B   a place where the music passes through the relative minor key.   Bar .... (2)

From bar 9 onwards

C   a harmonic interval of a minor 7th in the
right-hand part (circle the notes concerned).   Bar .... (2)

D   an upper auxiliary note in the right-hand part (circle the note concerned).   Bar .... (2)

E   a melodic interval of a diminished 3rd in the
right-hand inner part (circle the notes concerned).   Bar .... (2)

(e) Compare bars 12–13 with bars 13–14 (both marked ⌐﹍﹍﹍¬) and then name two similarities and three differences.

Similarities   1   .... (1)

               2   .... (1)

Differences   1   .... (1)

               2   .... (1)

               3   .... (1)

(f) From the list below, underline one period during which you think this piece was written.

        1600–1700   1700–1800   1800–1900 (1)

5 Look at the extract printed opposite, which is from the second movement of Lennox Berkeley's *Divertimento*, and then answer the questions below.

(a) Give the meaning of:

sul pont. (bar 4, violas) .... (2)

senza sord. (bar 6, trumpets) .... (2)

div. (bar 6, cellos) .... (2)

(b) (i) Write out the parts for horns in bar 2 as they would sound at concert pitch.

(2)

(ii) Write out the part for first clarinet in bar 6 as it would sound at concert pitch.

(2)

(c) Name two standard orchestral **non-transposing** instruments, one woodwind and one brass, **not** playing in this extract.

Woodwind .... Brass .... (2)

(d) Describe fully the numbered and bracketed harmonic intervals **sounding** between:

1 cellos and second bassoon, bar 1 .... (2)

2 violas (top note) and first trumpet, bar 5 .... (2)

(e) Write out the parts for bassoons in bars 2–3 so that they sound at the same pitch but using the given clef.

(3)

(f) Answer TRUE or FALSE to these statements:

(i) In bar 1, the harmonic intervals between the first and second bassoons are all major 3rds. .... (2)

(ii) The cellos and double basses **sound** in unison throughout bars 1–4. .... (2)

(iii) The cello has to use an open string in this extract. .... (2)

8

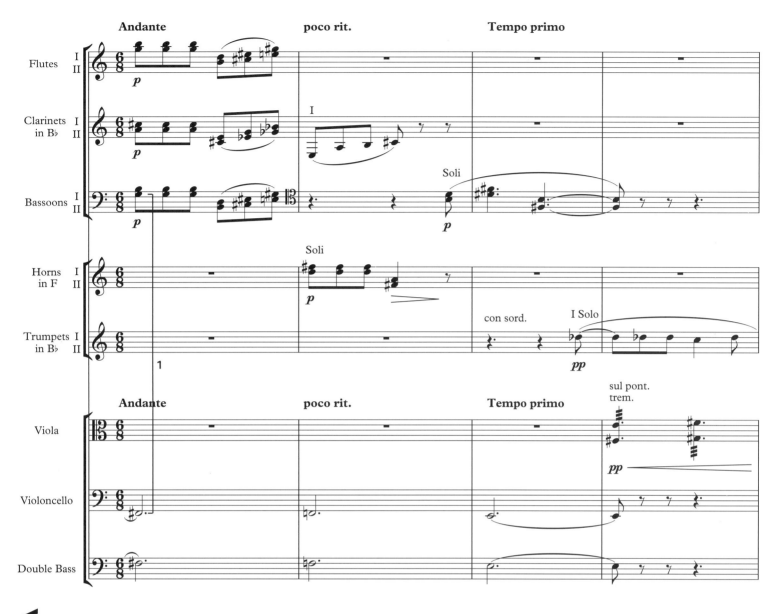

BLANK PAGE

Theory Paper   Grade 6   2018   B

Duration 3 hours

TOTAL MARKS
100

Candidates should answer all FIVE questions.
Write your answers on this paper – no others will be accepted.
Answers must be written clearly and neatly – otherwise marks may be lost.

1   Answer **ONE** section only, (a) or (b).

15

EITHER

(a)   Indicate **ONE** chord at each of the places marked * to accompany the following melody. You may do so by writing roman numerals or any other recognized method of notation between the staves, **OR** by writing notes on the staves which provide a proper harmonic structure; but use only **ONE** of these methods.

Croft, Organ Voluntary No. 12 in D (adapted)

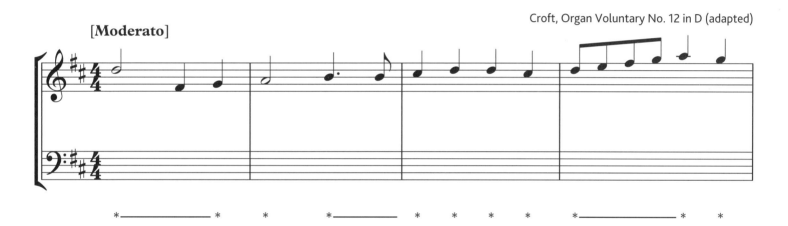

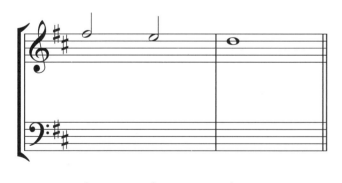

OR

(b) Complete the bass line and add a suitable figured bass as necessary, **from the first beat of bar 4**, at the places marked ∗ in this passage. If you wish to use a $\frac{5}{3}$ chord, leave the space under the asterisk blank, but $\frac{5}{3}$ chords **must** be shown when used as part of a $\frac{6}{4}\frac{5}{3}$ progression or when chromatic alteration is required.

[Moderato]

Montéclair, Cantata, 'Les délices champestres' (adapted)

2   Writing for four-part voices (SATB) or keyboard, realize this figured bass.
    Assume that all chords are $\frac{5}{3}$ unless otherwise shown.

15

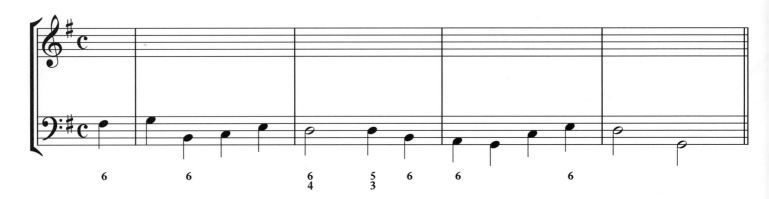

3 EITHER

(a) Continue this opening to form a complete melody for unaccompanied oboe. It should end with a modulation to the subdominant and should be between eight and ten bars long. Add performance directions as appropriate and write the complete melody on the staves below.

OR

(b) Continue this opening for unaccompanied bassoon to make a complete melody of not less than eight bars in length. You may make any modulation(s) that you wish, or none if you prefer. Add performance directions as appropriate and write the complete melody on the staves below.

4 Look at the extract printed opposite, which is from a sonata for violin and keyboard, and then answer the questions below.

(a) Identify the chords marked ∗ in bars 3 and 10 by writing on the dotted lines below. Use either words or symbols. For each chord, indicate the position and show whether it is major, minor, augmented or diminished.

Bar 3 .... Key   D minor (3)

Bar 10 .... Key   B♭ major (3)

(b) Write out in full the violin part of bar 7 as you think it should be played. Part of the bar is given.

(3)

(c) Mark **clearly** on the score, using the appropriate capital letter for identification, one example of each of the following. Also give the bar number(s) of each of your answers. The first answer is given.

From bar 9 onwards

A   a harmonic interval of a diminished 5th in the right-hand piano part (circle the notes concerned).   Bar ...21...

B   a melodic interval of an augmented 4th in the violin part (circle the notes concerned).   Bar .... (2)

C   two bars that form a rising sequence with the previous two bars (mark ⌐ C ¬ over the bars).   Bars .... (2)

D   an imperfect cadence in the tonic key.   Bars .... (2)

E   a grace note that forms the melodic interval of a major 2nd with the main note that follows it (circle the note concerned).   Bar .... (2)

(d) Give the full names of the notes of melodic decoration (e.g. note of anticipation) marked **X**, **Y** and **Z** in the violin part of bars 15 and 20.

X (bar 15) .... (2)

Y (bar 15) .... (2)

Z (bar 20) .... (2)

(e) Name two features of this extract that show it was written between 1700 and 1780.

1 .... (1)

2 .... (1)

5 Look at the extract printed opposite, which is from Fauré's suite *Pelléas et Mélisande*, and then answer the questions below.

(a) Give the meaning of:

+ (e.g. bar 4, first horn) .... (2)

con sord. (e.g. bar 9, first violins) .... (2)

arco (bar 11, cellos) .... (2)

(b) (i) Write out the parts for clarinets in bars 7–8 as they would sound at concert pitch and using the given clef.

Clarinets 1 / 2

(3)

(ii) The notes printed below are notated at written pitch for the first and second horns shortly after the extract ends. Write out the parts (for horns in F) as they would sound at concert pitch.

Horns (at written pitch) 1 / 2

Horns (at concert pitch) 1 / 2

(4)

(c) Mark **clearly** on the score, using the appropriate capital letter for identification, one example of each of the following. Also give the bar number(s) of each of your answers. The first answer is given.

From bar 4 onwards

A   an instruction for both players to play the same line.   Bar ....13....

B   a place where the violas have to use an open string (circle the note concerned).   Bar .... (2)

C   a melodic interval of an augmented 2nd in a clarinet part (circle the notes concerned).   Bars .... (2)

(d) Describe fully the numbered and bracketed harmonic intervals **sounding** between:

1   first horn and first clarinet, bar 4 .... (2)

2   double basses and flutes, bar 13 .... (2)

(e) Answer TRUE or FALSE to these statements:

(i)   In bars 1–5, the cellos and double basses **sound** an octave apart. .... (2)

(ii) The first violin and second violin parts cross in this extract. .... (2)

BLANK PAGE

Theory Paper   Grade 6   2018   C

Duration 3 hours

TOTAL MARKS
100

Candidates should answer all FIVE questions.
Write your answers on this paper – no others will be accepted.
Answers must be written clearly and neatly – otherwise marks may be lost.

1   Answer **ONE** section only, (a) or (b).

15

EITHER

(a) Indicate **ONE** chord at each of the places marked ∗ to accompany the following melody. You may do so by writing roman numerals or any other recognized method of notation between the staves, **OR** by writing notes on the staves which provide a proper harmonic structure; but use only **ONE** of these methods.

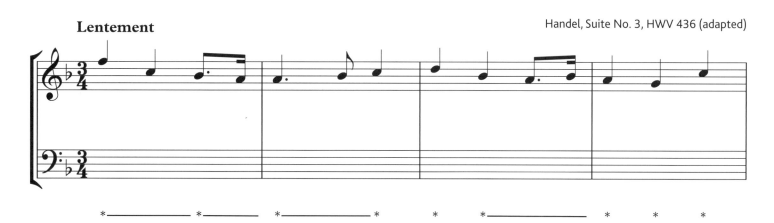

OR

(b) Complete the bass line and add a suitable figured bass as necessary, **from the last beat of bar 3**, at the places marked * in this passage. If you wish to use a $\frac{5}{3}$ chord, leave the space under the asterisk blank, but $\frac{5}{3}$ chords **must** be shown when used as part of a $\frac{6}{4}\frac{5}{3}$ progression or when chromatic alteration is required.

Telemann, Flute Concerto No. 6 in A minor, TWV 42 (adapted)

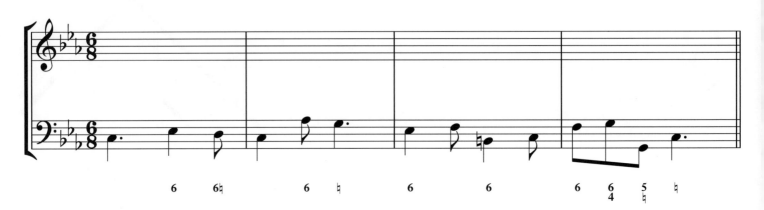

2 Writing for four-part voices (SATB) or keyboard, realize this figured bass.
   Assume that all chords are $\frac{5}{3}$ unless otherwise shown.

[15]

3 EITHER

(a) Continue this opening to form a complete melody for unaccompanied clarinet (at concert pitch). It should end with a modulation to the relative minor and should be between eight and ten bars long. Add performance directions as appropriate and write the complete melody on the staves below.

OR

(b) Continue this opening for unaccompanied cello to make a complete melody of not less than eight bars in length. You may make any modulation(s) that you wish, or none if you prefer. Add performance directions as appropriate and write the complete melody on the staves below.

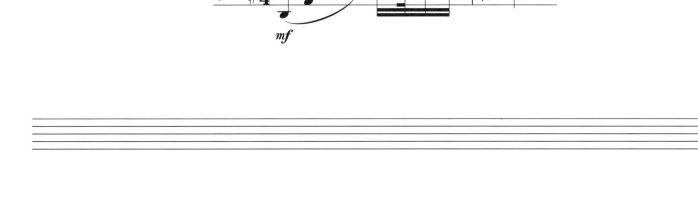

4 Look at the extract printed opposite, which is from a piano piece by Glazunov, and then answer the questions below.

25

(a) Give the meaning of *a piacere* (bar 1). .... (2)

(b) Identify the chords marked * in bars 14 and 15 (both shaded) by writing on the dotted lines below. Use either words or symbols. For each chord, indicate the position and show whether it is major, minor, augmented or diminished.

Bar 14 .... (3)

Bar 15 .... (3)

Key   E minor

(c) Mark **clearly** on the score, using the appropriate capital letter for identification, one example of each of the following. Also give the bar number of each of your answers. The first answer is given.

In bars 1–16

A a descending chromatic semitone
(augmented unison) in the right-hand part (circle the notes concerned).   Bar ......4......

B a perfect cadence in the relative minor key.   Bar .... (2)

C arpeggiation of a major triad in first inversion
in the left-hand part (circle the notes concerned).   Bar .... (2)

D a harmonic interval of a major 7th in the
left-hand part (circle the notes concerned).   Bar .... (2)

(d) Give the full names of the notes of melodic decoration (e.g. note of anticipation) marked **X**, **Y** and **Z**.

X (right-hand part, bar 5)   .... (2)

Y (right-hand part, bar 20)   .... (2)

Z (left-hand part, bar 22)   .... (2)

(e) Compare bar 13 with bar 17 (both marked ⌐‾‾‾‾⌐) and then name one similarity and two differences.

Similarity   .... (1)

Differences   1   .... (1)

2   .... (1)

(f) Complete this statement:

The largest melodic interval in the
top line of the right-hand part is a(n) .... (2)

5 Look at the extract printed on pages 25–26, which is from Kodály's *Dances of Galánta*, and then answer the questions below.

(a) Give the meaning of:

tr〰〰 (e.g. bar 3, clarinet) .... (2)

poco stringendo (bar 7) .... (2)

pizz. (e.g. bar 7, violas) .... (2)

(b) (i) Write out the parts for horns in bar 1 as they would sound at concert pitch.

(3)

(ii) Write out the part for clarinet in bars 3–4 (without the ornament) as it would sound at concert pitch.

(4)

(c) Describe fully the numbered and bracketed harmonic intervals **sounding** between:

1 cellos and second violins, bar 4 .... (2)

2 violas and second oboe, bar 7 .... (2)

3 upper second violins and clarinet, bar 7 .... (2)

(d) Answer TRUE or FALSE to these statements:

(i) The first bassoon and violas sound in unison on the first beat of bar 1. .... (2)

(ii) The cellos are the only instruments that have to use an open string in this extract. .... (2)

(iii) The letter name of the highest note played by the first violins is F♯. .... (2)

Turn the page

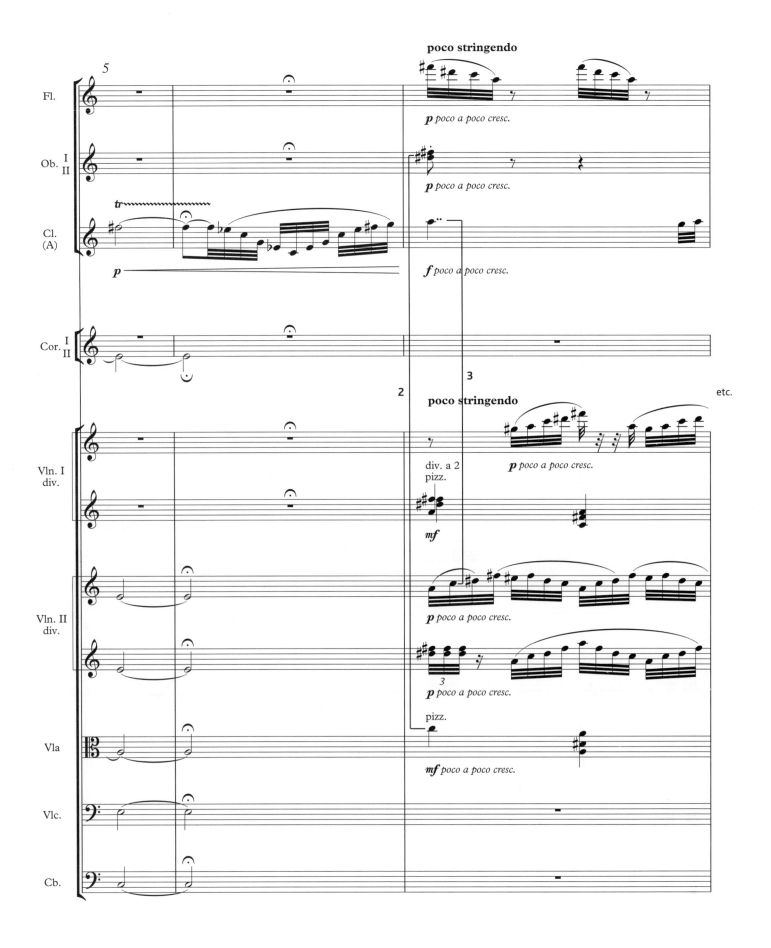

26

Theory Paper   Grade 6   2018   S

Duration 3 hours

TOTAL MARKS
100

Candidates should answer all FIVE questions.
Write your answers on this paper – no others will be accepted.
Answers must be written clearly and neatly – otherwise marks may be lost.

1 Answer **ONE** section only, (a) or (b).

15

EITHER

(a) Indicate **ONE** chord at each of the places marked * to accompany the following melody. You may do so by writing roman numerals or any other recognized method of notation between the staves, **OR** by writing notes on the staves which provide a proper harmonic structure; but use only **ONE** of these methods.

Stanley, Voluntary in F, Op. 7 No. 10 (adapted)

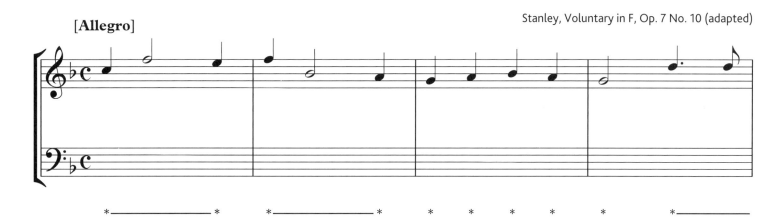

OR

(b) Complete the bass line and add a suitable figured bass as necessary, **from the first beat of bar 5**, at the places marked ∗ in this passage. If you wish to use a $^5_3$ chord, leave the space under the asterisk blank, but $^5_3$ chords **must** be shown when used as part of a $^{6\;5}_{4\;3}$ progression or when chromatic alteration is required.

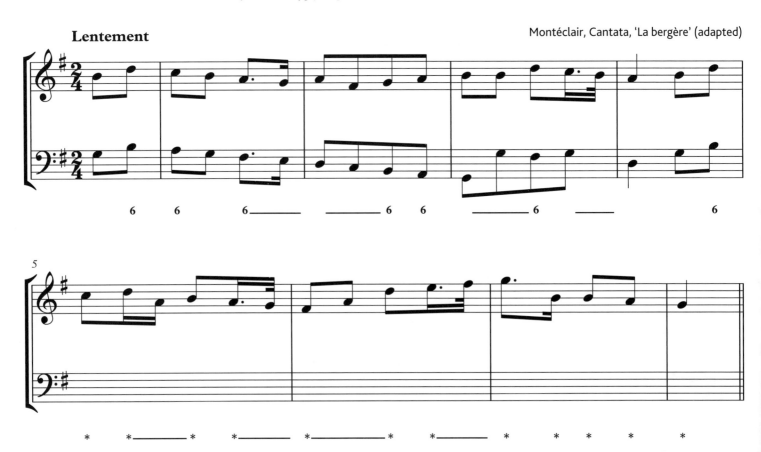

2 Writing for four-part voices (SATB) or keyboard, realize this figured bass. Assume that all chords are $^5_3$ unless otherwise shown.

15

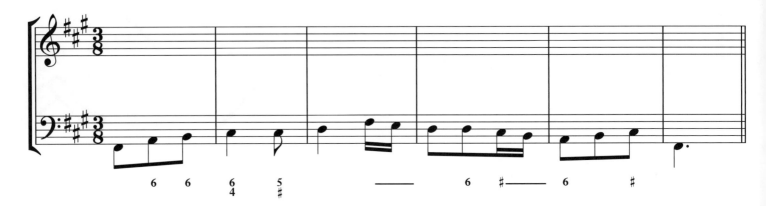

3 EITHER

(a) Continue this opening to form a complete melody for unaccompanied trumpet (at concert pitch). It should end with a modulation to the relative minor and should be between eight and ten bars long. Add performance directions as appropriate and write the complete melody on the staves below.

OR

(b) Continue this opening for unaccompanied cello to make a complete melody of not less than eight bars in length. You may make any modulation(s) that you wish, or none if you prefer. Add performance directions as appropriate and write the complete melody on the staves below.

4 Look at the extract printed opposite, which is from a keyboard sonata by C. P. E. Bach, and then answer the questions below.

(a) Identify the chords marked ∗ in bars 9 and 25 (shaded) by writing on the dotted lines below. Use either words or symbols. For each chord, indicate the position and show whether it is major, minor, augmented or diminished.

Bar 9 .... Key B♭ major (3)

Bar 25 .... Key A minor (3)

(b) Mark **clearly** on the score, using the appropriate capital letter for identification, one example of each of the following. Also give the bar number of each of your answers. The first answer is given.

In bars 1–16

A a written-out turn in the right-hand part (circle the notes concerned). Bar ......7......

B a bar in which **all** the notes can be found in the dominant 7th chord (V⁷) of the dominant minor key. Bar .... (2)

C syncopation in the right-hand part. Bar .... (2)

D a harmonic interval of a compound augmented 2nd between the right-hand and left-hand parts (circle the notes concerned). Bar .... (2)

E a harmonic interval of a major 3rd in the left-hand part (circle the notes concerned). Bar .... (2)

F a rising chromatic semitone (augmented unison) in the left-hand part (circle the notes concerned). Bar .... (2)

(c) Write out in full the right-hand part of bar 6 as you think it should be played. Part of the bar is given.

(3)

(d) Give the full names of the notes of melodic decoration (e.g. upper auxiliary note) marked **X**, **Y** and **Z** in the right-hand part of bars 22, 24 and 26.

X (bar 22) .... (2)

Y (bar 24) .... (2)

Z (bar 26) .... (2)

5 Look at the extract printed on pages 33–34, which is from Butterworth's *A Shropshire Lad*, and then answer the questions below.

(a) Give the meaning of:

$\overset{\equiv}{\circ}$ (e.g. bar 1, double basses) .... (2)

con sord. (bar 2, horns) .... (2)

muta G in A (bar 5, timpani) .... (2)

glissando (bar 6, harp) .... (2)

(b) (i) Write out the parts for horns in bar 2 as they would sound at concert pitch and using the given clefs.

(4)

(ii) Write out the parts for clarinets in bars 3–5 as they would sound at concert pitch.

(2)

(c) Describe fully the numbered and bracketed harmonic intervals **sounding** between:

1   violas and cor anglais, bar 1 .... (2)

2   cellos and second bassoon, bar 5 .... (2)

3   fourth horn and first oboe, bar 6 .... (2)

(d) Complete these statements:

(i) In bar 2, the cor anglais **sounds** in unison with the .... (2)

(ii) The only string section that plays
a double stop in this extract is the .... (2)

(iii) A standard orchestral **transposing** brass
instrument **not** playing in this extract is the .... (1)

Turn the page

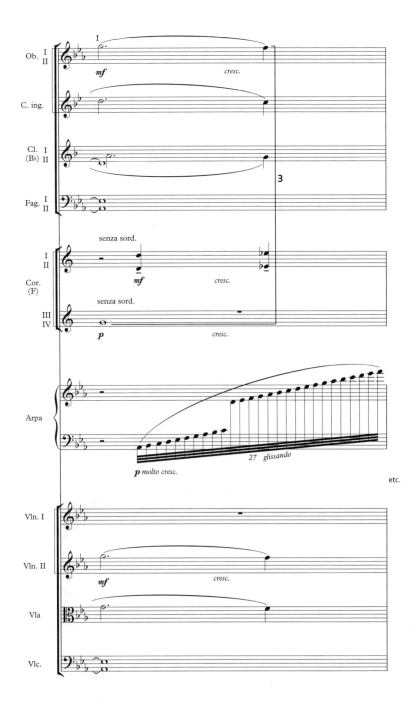